Red Bea
the Pirate

Written by Lisa Thompson
Pictures by Craig Smith and Lew Keilar

Stanley is a pirate captain.

The crew calls him Captain Red Beard, and he sails the seas in his pirate ship called *The Black Beast*.

Captain Red Beard's crew is a funny bunch, but he could not sail his ship without them.

Fingers, the parrot, knows how to read maps.

Busy Lizzie is the first mate. She tells the crew what their jobs are every day.

Bones, the sea dog, looks out for rocks, land and other ships.

5

Captain Red Beard loves sailing his pirate ship, even when a storm comes and makes the waves look like mountains.

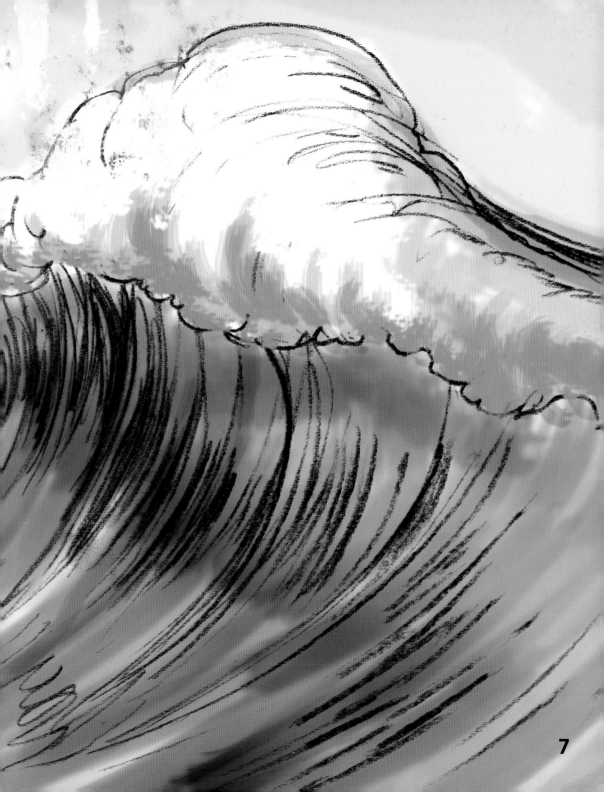

Captain Red Beard loves to meet other pirates, but they don't enjoy meeting him!

"Fire the cannons!" he shouts. "Down she goes!"

Captain Red Beard loves giving orders.

"Scrub the decks! Mend those sails!
Get me my parrot! Tighten the rigging!"

His crew often has better things to do.

Captain Red Beard loves swinging in his hammock, singing songs of the sea and playing his guitar.

He cannot sing in tune, but he knows hundreds of jolly songs.

13

While the crew eats dinner, the Captain shines his boots, and tells them long, pirate stories.

Lizzie thinks his stories are very funny, but the rest of the crew wish he would clean his boots in the hold.

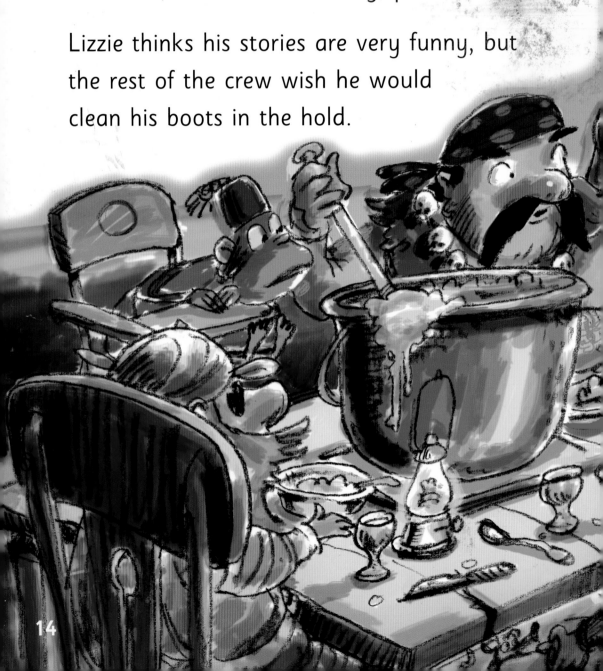

Captain Red Beard loves to look very smart and very fierce.

He looks in the mirror to check his pirate hat. He brushes his red beard, and puts on a new eye patch every day.

"Flying cannonballs!" he cries.
"Watch out for fierce Red Beard."

Captain Red Beard loves shooting the cannons and flying his pirate flag.

Best of all, Captain Red Beard
loves hunting for treasure.

He searches and searches for treasure.

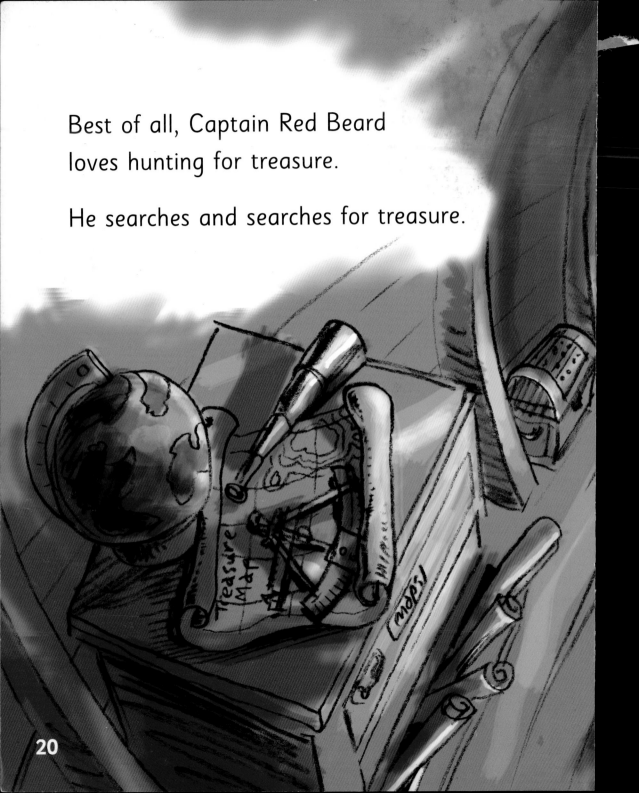

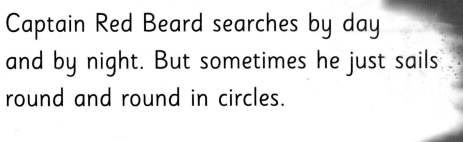

Captain Red Beard searches by day
and by night. But sometimes he just sails
round and round in circles.

Perhaps he should let Fingers,
the parrot, read the maps!